The Parable of
the Rich Fool

Text copyright © Daniel Collins 1995

Published by
Barnabas
an imprint of
The Bible Reading Fellowship
Peter's Way,
Sandy Lane West,
Oxford,
OX4 5HG
ISBN 0 7459 3086 7
Albatross Books Pty Ltd
PO Box 320,
Sutherland,
NSW 2232,
Australia
ISBN 0 7324 0916 0

First edition 1995
10 9 8 7 6 5 4 3 2 1 0

A catalogue record for this book is available
from the British Library

Barnabas ™ is a trademark of The Bible Reading Fellowship

Printed and bound in Hong Kong

The Parable
of the Rich Fool

But then he began to think to himself.

And he had a fantastic idea.

And he said to himself greedily:

So he thought of how he could enjoy life and do what he liked.

And then Jesus concluded, and said:

THE PAINTBOX SERIES

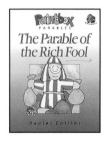

Available from your local bookshop or,
in case of difficulty, direct from BRF.